A BIG BALL OF STRING

A small string ball is no good at all.
But after our hero takes a trip to the
dump, he finds lots
and LOTS
of things
with STRINGS!
And before long, he's got a BIG ball
of string, and with a BIG ball of
string you can do anything, anything, ANYTHING at all!

Beginning readers will be eager to
follow the antics of this inventive
hero, page after page. And they can!
Because the short sentences and
spirited rhyme will have them read-
ing *all by themselves!*

This book comes from
the home of
THE CAT IN THE HAT
Beginner Books
A DIVISION OF RANDOM HOUSE, INC.

*For a list of some other Beginner
Books, see the back endpaper.*

To NICK and ANDREW

Text copyright © 1958, renewed 1986 by Marion Holland
Illustrations copyright © 1993 by Roy McKie

All rights reserved.
Published in the United States by Random House Children's Books,
a division of Random House, Inc., New York.

BEGINNER BOOKS, RANDOM HOUSE, and the Random House colophon are
registered trademarks of Random House, Inc. THE CAT IN THE HAT logo
® and © Dr. Seuss Enterprises, L.P. 1957, renewed 1986. All rights reserved.

Visit us on the Web! www.randomhouse.com/kids

Educators and librarians, for a variety of teaching tools, visit us at
www.randomhouse.com/teachers

The Library of Congress has cataloged the hardcover edition of this work as follows:
Holland, Marion.
A big ball of string / by Marion Holland ; illustrated by Roy McKie.
p. cm.
SUMMARY: After winding a large ball of string, a young boy has fun
finding ways of using it.
ISBN 978-0-394-80005-9 (trade) — ISBN 978-0-394-90005-6 (lib. bdg.)
[1. Stories in rhyme.] I. McKie, Roy, ill. II. Title. PZ8.3.H699Bi
1993 [E]—dc20 92-16355

ISBN: 978-0-375-87499-4 (pbk.)

Printed in the United States of America
10 9 8 7 6 5 4 3 2 1

A BIG BALL OF STRING

By Marion Holland

Illustrated by Roy McKie

Beginner Books   A Division of Random House, Inc.

I had a little string.

It was no good at all.

I went to look for more string

To make a string ball.

I got more string

From a box in the hall.

I made it all up

In a little string ball.

But what could I DO
With a little ball of string?
What could I do
With a SMALL string ball?
With a BIG ball of string,
I could do ANYTHING.
Anything, anything,
ANYTHING AT ALL!

My mother has string.

Look what a lot!

Did she give ME some of it?

She did NOT.

"Stay OUT
Of my things!"
Mother said,
With a frown.
"You can NOT
Have those strings.
Put them down!
Put them down!"

And my daddy has string.

Look what a lot!

Did he give ME some of it?

He did NOT.

"That is NOT a toy!
Put it down!"
Said Dad.

And—boy, oh, boy!
Was
    my
        dad
            MAD!

So I went out back,

To the big old cans.

There were socks and sacks,

And pots and pans.

I looked and looked.

And what did I see?

Strings and STRINGS,

And all for me!

But—here came a man,
And he shook out the can.

He shook all the things
From the can in a sack.
He took all the things
In a pack on his back.

"Hey! You with the sack!
You bring back my string!"

He did NOT bring it back.

He did not say a thing.

Away went the man.

Away went the truck.

And away I went!
And then—what luck!

BUMPETY-BUMP!

The truck dumped

With a thump.

And there I was

At the good old dump!

With bags of rags,

And old tin cans.

And mops and mats,

And pots and pans.

And jacks and tires,

And sacks and wires.

And cots and springs—

And lots

And LOTS

Of things

With STRINGS!

I put all the string
On my little string ball.
I made me the BIGGEST
String ball of all.

My ball was so big!
As big as my head!
And I looked
At my big ball of string,
And I said,

"NOW I will find
A thing of some kind—
Some GOOD kind of thing
To do with my string!"

I had a balloon like a pig

From the zoo.

My balloon was so red and so big

And so new

That I said, "NOW I know

What will be a good thing!"

And I let my pig go

Up, up, UP, with my string!

It went up so high

It was something to see!

As high as a house!

As high as a tree!

As high as the sky!

And I said, "Stop! Stop!

You are up TOO HIGH!"

And then, something went—

It went POP, like that!

My big red pig!

Then it was not fat,

Or red, or big.

It was all in bits,

And the bits fell on me.

And the string fell, too,

And got stuck in a tree.

So I went up the tree
To get down my string.
And I said, "Now I see
That was NOT a good thing!"

But I did not mind.
I KNEW I could find
Some good kind of thing
To do with my string.

So I got my string down
And I made a machine,
With a bike and a trike
And a jeep in between.

And I sat way up top,

On a box with a mop,

On the jeep in between,

And I ran the machine!

Then the bike hit a bump.

And the jeep gave a jump.

And the trike hit a tree.

And the box

And the mop

Came down,

KER-FLOP!

Came down

On top

Of ME!

So I got a big bump
On the top of my head.
And it made a big lump.
And I sat there and said,
"That was NOT a good thing
To do with my string,
With my string in a ball.
Not a good thing AT ALL!"

But I did not mind.
I KNEW I would find
Some good kind of thing
To do with my string.

Then I went up to bed.

"Tomorrow," I said,

"I will take my string out.

I will look all about.

I will FIND a good thing

To do with my string.

That is what I will do

Tomorrow," I said.

And I lay down to sleep,

With my string on my bed.

But THEN I woke up
With a cold in my head.

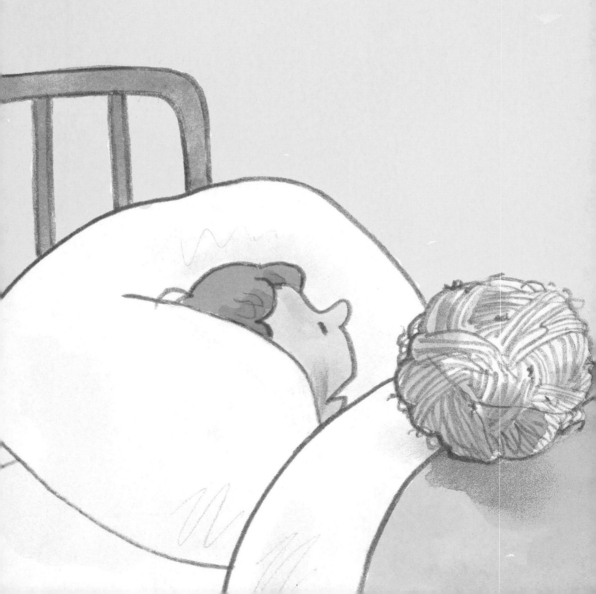

And my mother came in,
And she said,
"Stay in bed.
With a cold in your head,
Stay in bed!
Stay in bed!"

I shot all my darts
At the wall, and I said,
"Now how can I get them,
And stay in my bed?"

Then I looked at my string,

At my big ball of string.

And I said,

"NOW I know

What will be a good thing!

I can stay

In my bed

With my big ball of string!

I can play

In my bed!

I can do ANYTHING!"

With my string on my darts,

I can shoot them away!

I can get them all back!

I can do it all day!

I can shoot them about,

At the door,

At the wall.

I can shoot them all out

On the floor

In the hall!

I can shoot all my darts.
But—when they are shot,
I MAY want to look
At some books
I have got.

I can rig up a thing
With a box and a hook
And my big ball of string.
It will bring me a book.
And I can have fun
With my books
In my bed,
With my string,
And my gun,
And my cold in the head!

But the light should be right
When I look at my book.

I can pull up the blind
On this good sunny day.
I can turn on the light
If the sun goes away.
I can look at my book.
I can stay in my bed
With my gun, and my string,
And my cold in the head.

Then—I MAY want the cat.

She will come to the door.

She will jump at the mouse

On the string on the floor.

If I pull the door shut,

She can NOT run away.

I can play with the cat

In my bed all the day.

With my cat, and my gun,
And my books in my bed,
I can have lots of fun
With a cold in my head.

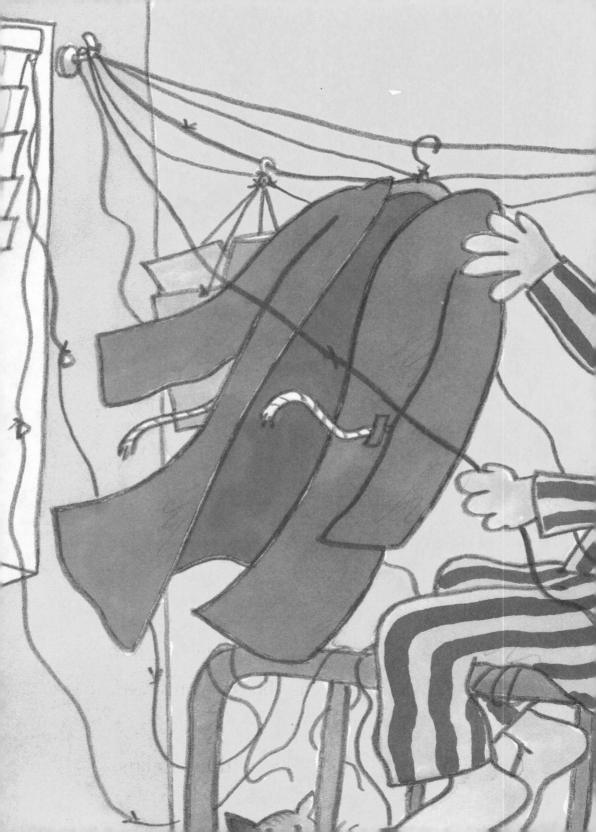

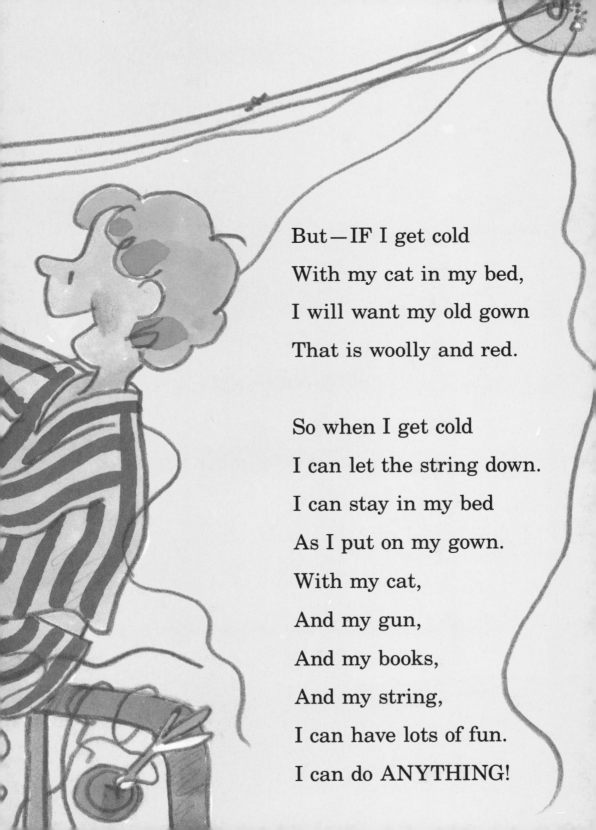

But—IF I get cold
With my cat in my bed,
I will want my old gown
That is woolly and red.

So when I get cold
I can let the string down.
I can stay in my bed
As I put on my gown.
With my cat,
And my gun,
And my books,
And my string,
I can have lots of fun.
I can do ANYTHING!

In my bed
With my string,
I can make my train go.
I can make it go fast.
I can make it go slow.

In my bed
With my books,
And my train on a string,
And my cat, and my gun,
I can do ANYTHING!

I will stay in my bed,

And I WILL not get out.

If I want anything

I will NOT run about.

I can rig up my bell

With my big ball of string.

My mother will come

When she hears the bell ring.

And THEN she will see

How I stay in my bed

With my strings,

And my things,

And my cold in the head!

Then Mother called up
To my room,
And she said,
"How is your cold?
DID YOU STAY IN YOUR BED?"

"Yes, Mother,"
I said.
And I JUMPED into bed.

I jumped into bed
With my string in a ball.
With my string,
With my string,
I can do ANYTHING.
Anything, anything,
ANYTHING AT ALL!

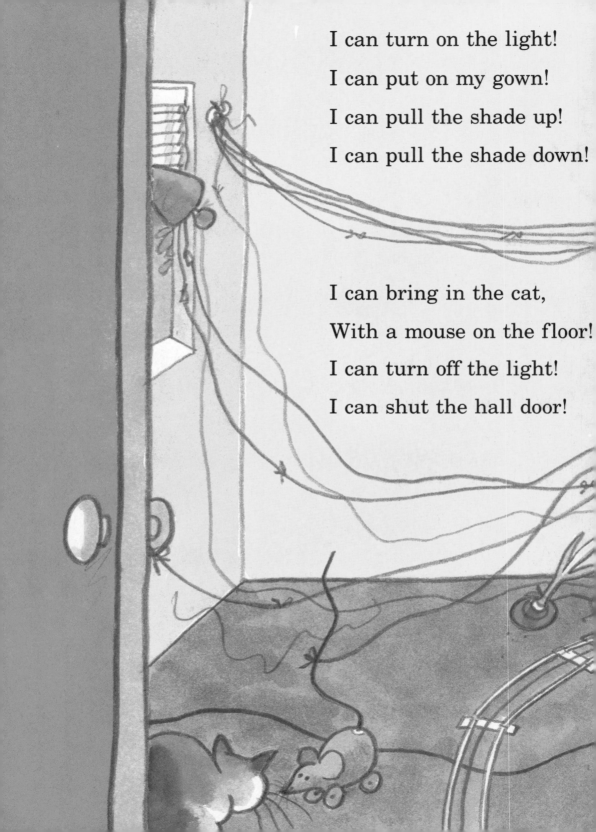

I can turn on the light!

I can put on my gown!

I can pull the shade up!

I can pull the shade down!

I can bring in the cat,

With a mouse on the floor!

I can turn off the light!

I can shut the hall door!

I can look at my book!

I can shoot with my gun!

I make my bell ring!

I can make my train run!

"Look, Mother!

Look, Mother!

LOOK, MOTHER!"

I said.

"Come and look,

Come and look,

How I stay in my bed,

With my strings,

And my things,

And my cold in the head!"

I can stay

In my bed.

I can play

In my bed.

I CAN DO ANYTHING

WITH A BIG BALL OF STRING!

Some Recent Beginner Books®

THE CAT'S QUIZZER
by Dr. Seuss

I AM <u>NOT</u> GOING TO GET UP TODAY!
by Dr. Seuss

I WANT TO BE SOMEBODY NEW!
by Robert Lopshire

THE VERY BAD BUNNY
by Marilyn Sadler

OH SAY CAN YOU SAY?
by Dr. Seuss

I CAN READ WITH MY EYES SHUT!
by Dr. Seuss

Some Recent Bright and Early Books®

THE BERENSTAIN BEARS ON THE MOON
by Stan and Jan Berenstain

THE TOOTH BOOK
by Theo. LeSieg

THE BERENSTAIN BEARS AND THE SPOOKY OLD TREE
by Stan and Jan Berenstain

GREAT DAY FOR UP
by Dr. Seuss

THERE'S A WOCKET IN MY POCKET!
by Dr. Seuss